NerdyBaby™

The world's most ridiculously excellent...
Science
coloring & activity book

SUPER SCIENCEY!
For humans who love astronomy, biology, chemistry, physics, neuroscience, geology, paleontology, zoology, mathematics, engineering and/or coloring.

The coloring book you are holding right now is made of ATOMS. And the crayons or markers you might use? Made of atoms! Can you guess what you are made of?

A atom

This is not what atoms look like. It's hard to draw atoms because they're so tiny. A physicist named Neils Bohr started drawing atoms like this. Scientists now know that Bohr's model is too simple, but it's still the most fun way to draw atoms.

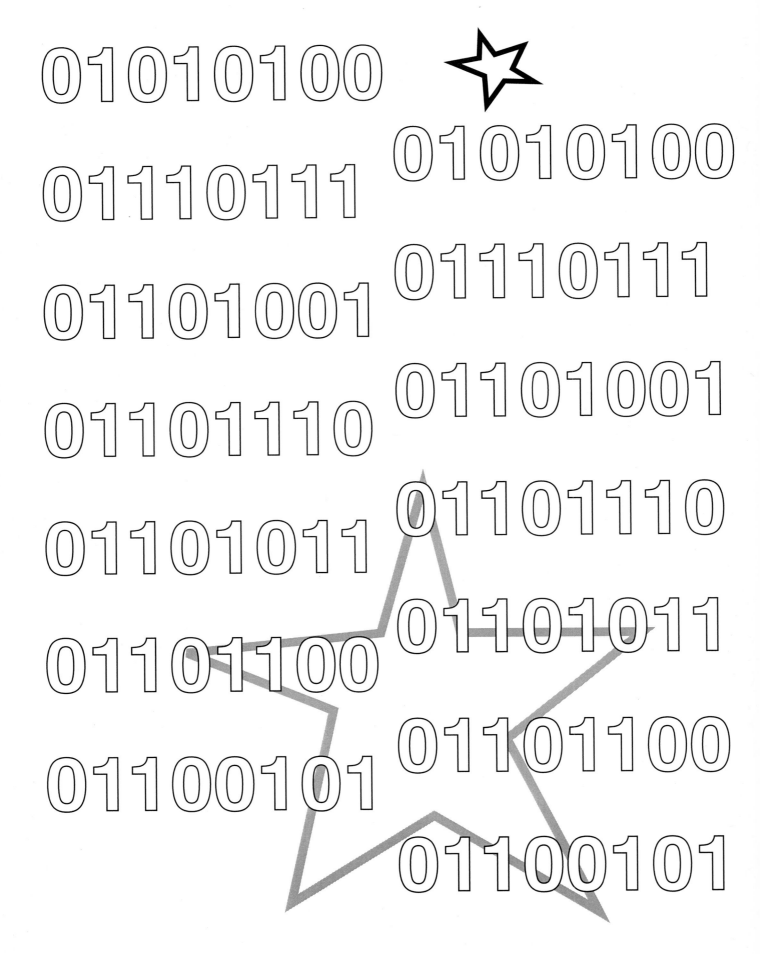

0110 1100

0110 1001

B

0110 0100

0111 0100

0110 1100

0110 0101

binary

0110 0011

0110 0100

0100 0001

0110 0010

A Binary Code is any code that turns information into only two signals. Perfect for when you need to say something using a ninja signal mirror or an electrical on-off switch.

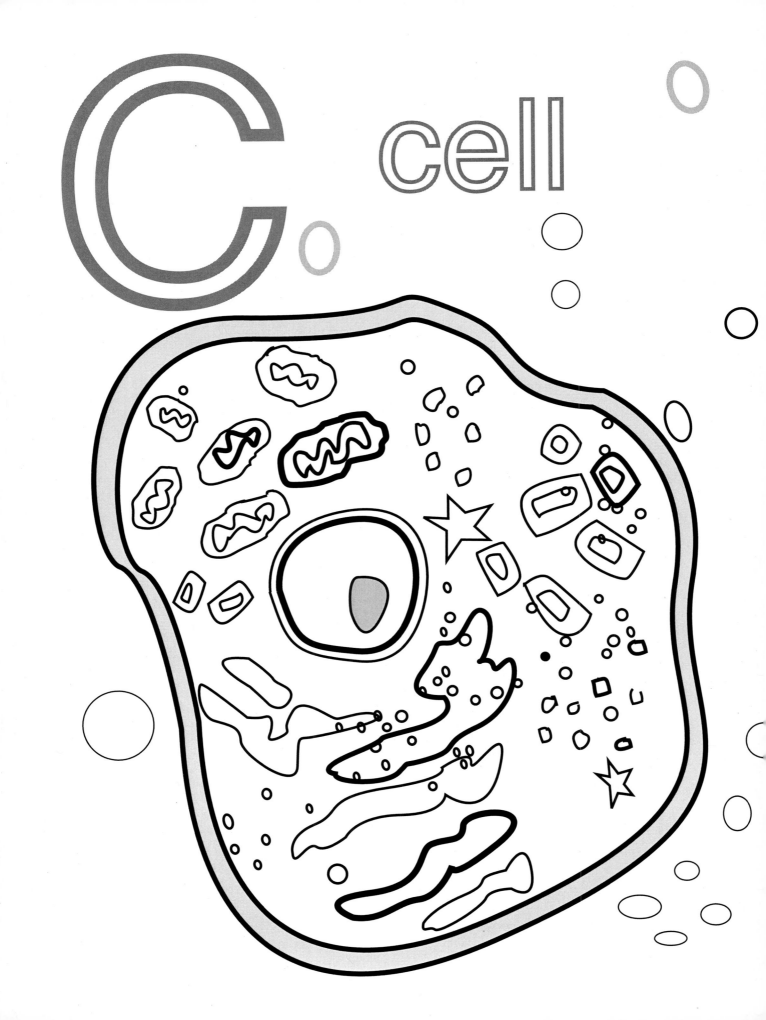

C. cell

All living things are made of cells! Cells hold water, store energy, process food, divide and work together to build some very interesting plants and animals.

Can you guess which of these silly-sounding words are NOT real names of parts of a cell?

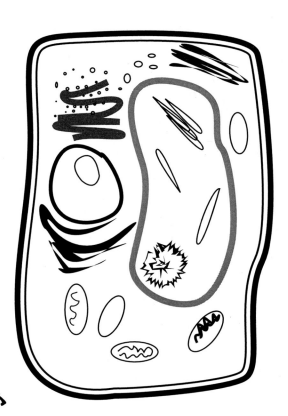

centipede finial

Vacuoles

centrioles

Endoplasmic reticulum

Filligree Spheroid

Cytoplasm

Bichon Frise

Golgi Apparatus

Ribosome

Gorgeous Vehicle

Paul Dirac was an interesting fellow. He was shy and didn't like to talk very much. Instead he liked to sit quietly by himself and think about the universe. He predicted the existence of antimatter, was one of the founders of quantum mechanics and came up with a useful thing called the Dirac Equation.

Great work, Dirac!

Enrico Fermi was a busy, busy person. He figured out lots of amazing tricks that you can do with atoms! Well, not YOU. You should never play with nuclear reactors or atomic bombs unless that's your job and you have security clearance.

When most people lose a bet they might have to pay a little bit of money or shave their hair off. Well, one day a physicist made a bet. If he lost, he had to promise that he would use the word "penguin" in his next official serious academic paper. Guess what? He lost the bet.

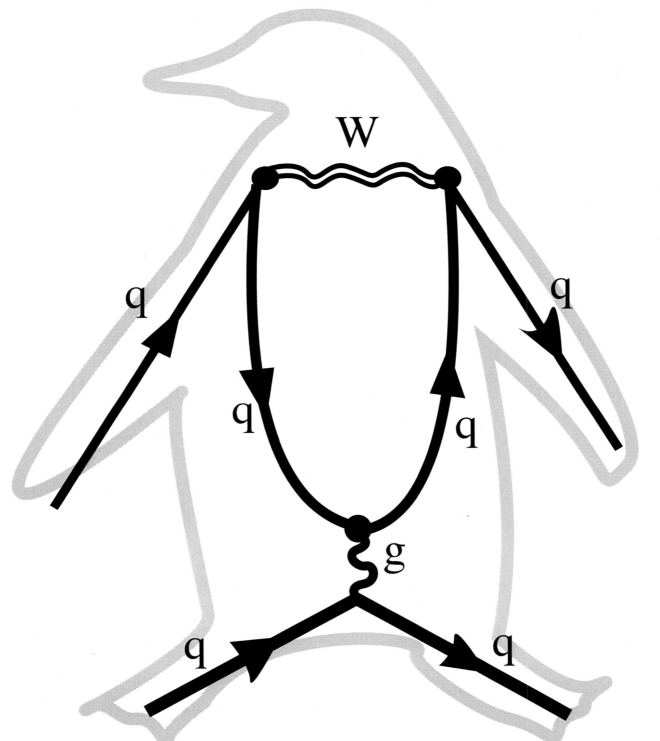

He didn't know how he was going to do it! Physics is not biology or zoology or penguinology. Then late one night he noticed that the Feynman diagram he was using looked a little bit like a penguin. He described it that way in his paper, and now this is officially called the penguin diagram.

I bet you can draw an animal around this diagram and give it a name.

D

diurnal

Nocturnal creatures sleep all day and run around all night. Diurnal animals sleep at night and run around playing and working all day. Are you nocturnal or diurnal?

E

Did you know that you can use electricity to make a magnet? And guess what! You can also use a magnet to make electricity! Isn't that weird?

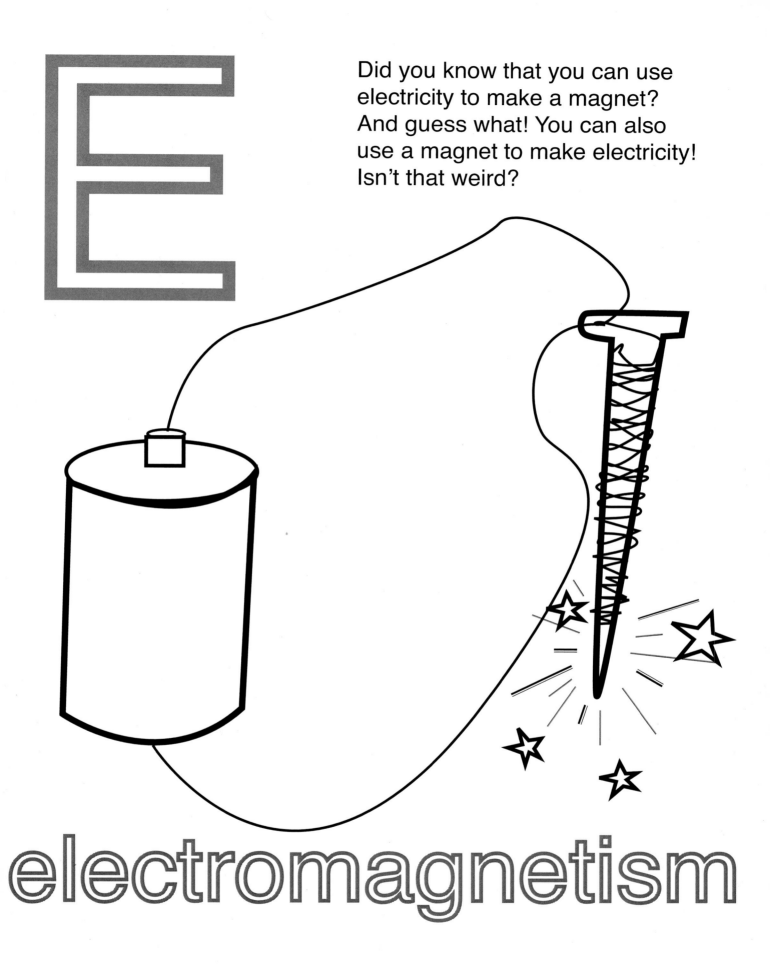

electromagnetism

STOP. Grammar Time!

Sometimes Grammar Bunny corrects his friends ...

...but he also lets the rules slide now and then.

Color the light bulb that could light up!

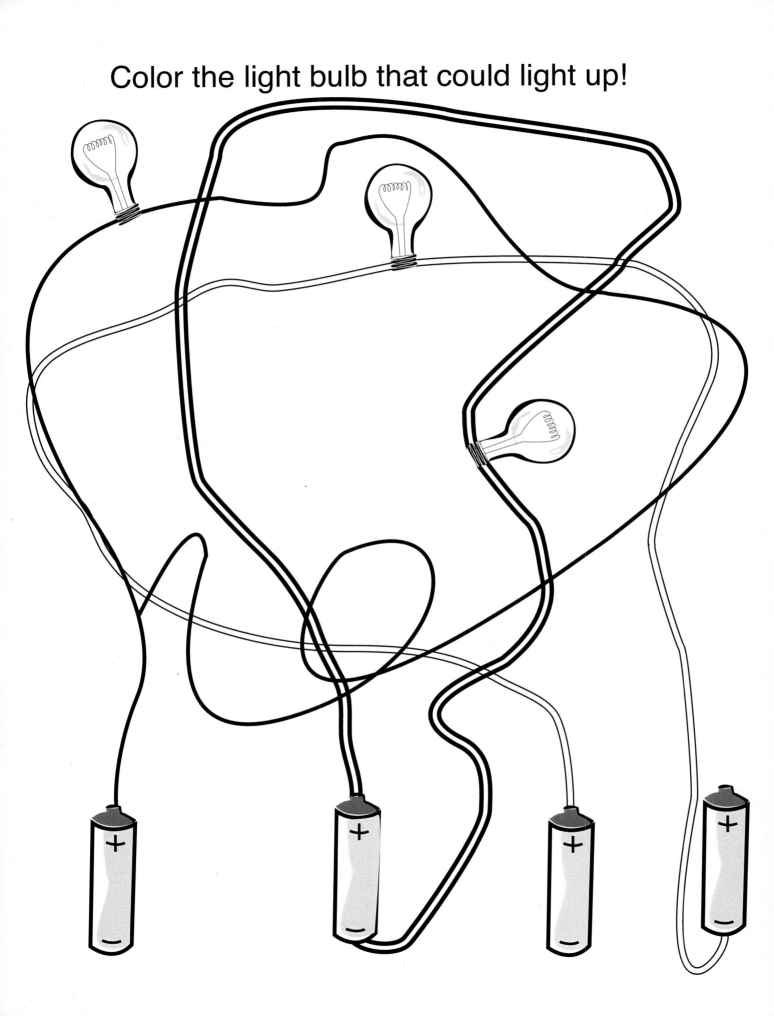

F

Big important scientists go to big important schools to get big important degrees so they can get big important jobs taking care of tiny ordinary old fruit flies. What?! Fruit flies? That's right, fruit flies. Turns out that these common little insects are amazing and useful for genetic research.

fruit fly

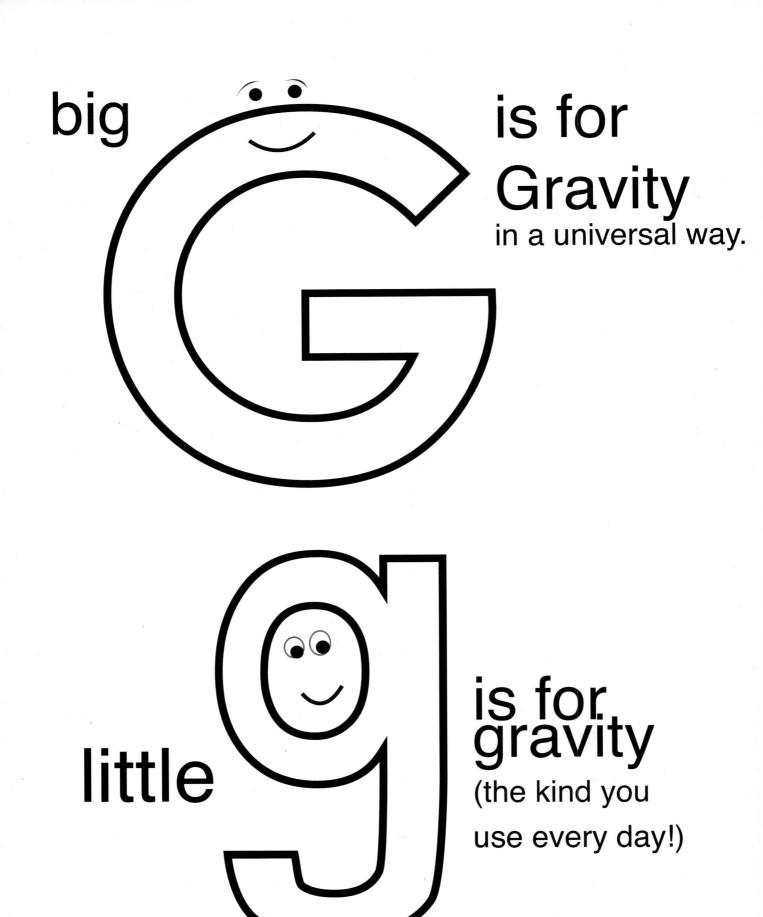

big **G** is for Gravity
in a universal way.

little **g** is for gravity
(the kind you use every day!)

glacier G

A glacier is a massive sheet of ice that creeps and slides around the earth during ice ages. As they move, glaciers slowly crush, smash, and slice through dirt and rocks that are in their way. They can carve beautiful valleys, riverbeds, and lakes. Go, glaciers!

(good for taking bites out of something round)

(great for quick and accurate grabbing)

(ideal for pulling and/or mashing)

(perfect for scooping stuff off the ground)

Can you help each finch decide what to eat?

Galapagos Cafe Menu

Diurnal meals served all day

Beautiful berries

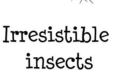

Irresistible insects

Luscious leaves

Fantastic Fruit

Great-tasting grubs

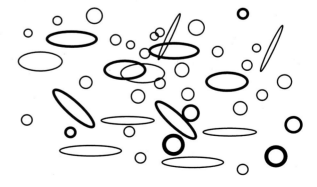

Scrumptious seeds

H

When water molecules start hugging each other, it takes a lot of energy to pull them apart.

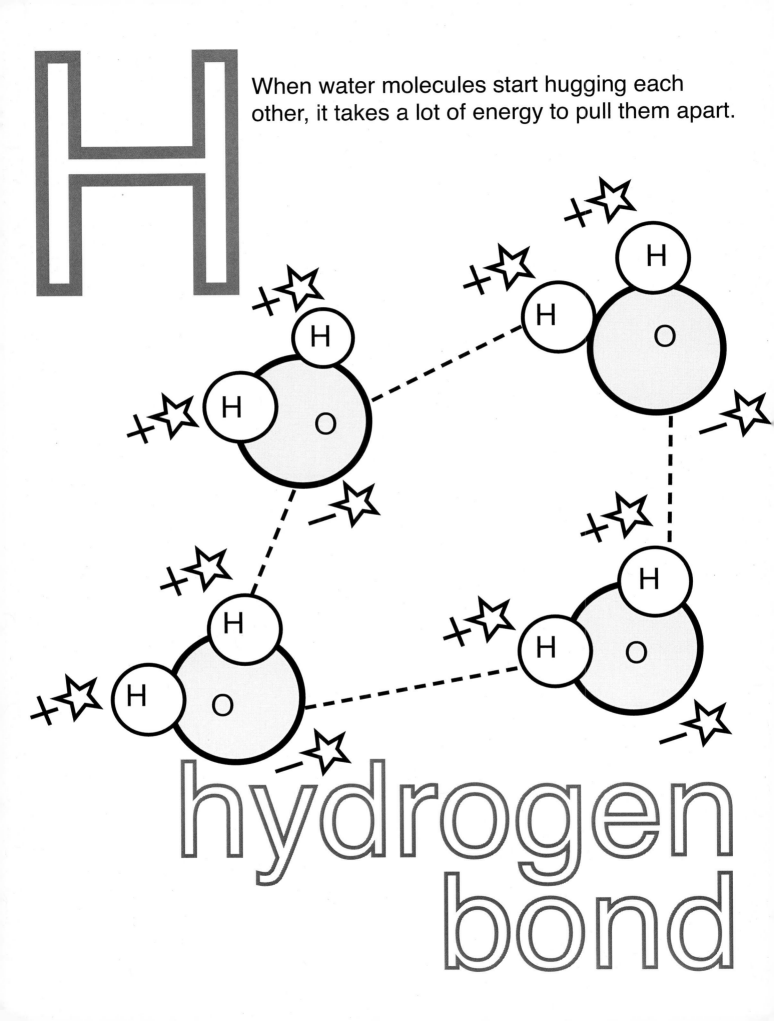

hydrogen bond

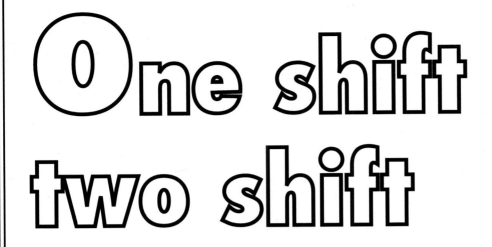

One shift
two shift

red shift

Blue shift

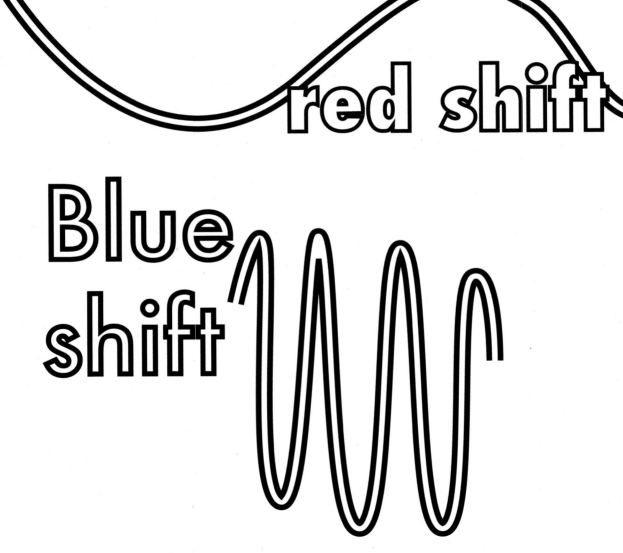

$$6.62606896 \times 10^{-34} \text{Js}$$

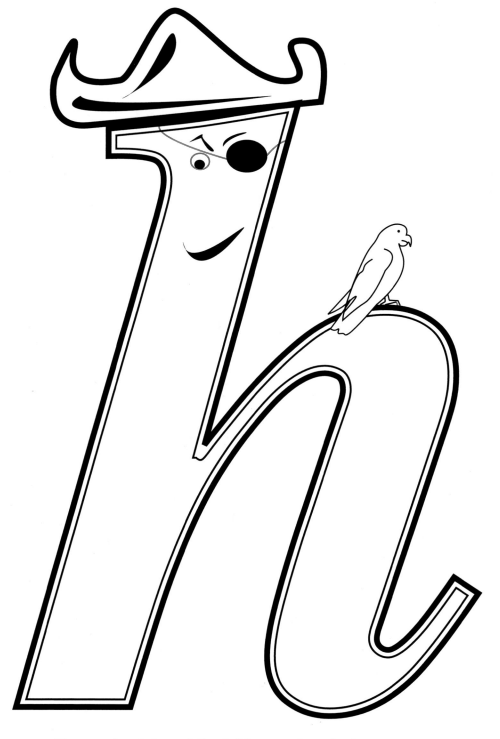

Captain Max Karl Ernst Ludwig says,
"Yar! I'll make you walk the Planck!"

Ichthyosaur

Ichthys means fish but ichthyosaur was not a fish. *Osaur* means lizard, which makes even less sense. Icthyosaur was not a fish, or a lizard, or a dinosaur. Ichthyosaur was an air-breathing reptile whose ancestors walked on land. Does Ichthyosaur remind you of another kind of ocean animal that lives today?

No one knows for sure what's inside the Earth!

Geologists have guesses. Do you have a guess? What do you think we'd find if we could dig down to the center of the earth?

Jupiter is the greediest planet! The Jovian system has jillions of moons. The biggest four of Jupiter's moons have beautiful names: Calisto, Ganymede, Io, and Europa.

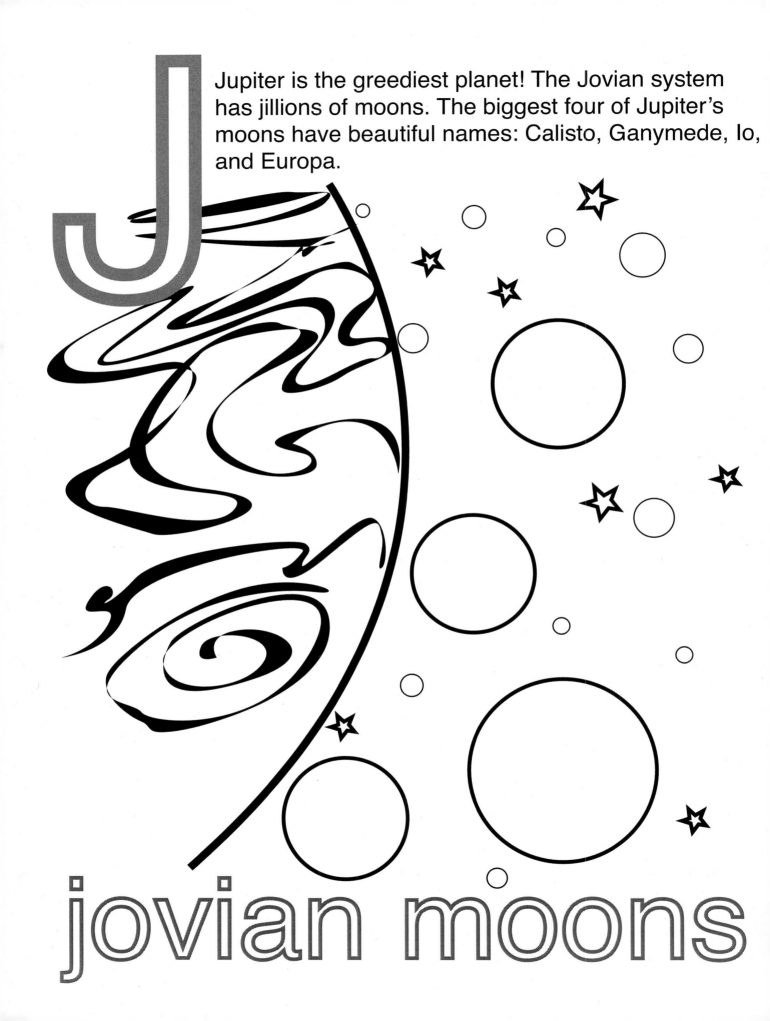

jovian moons

How scared should Mr.Bunny be?
Assign values to each variable and then calculate!

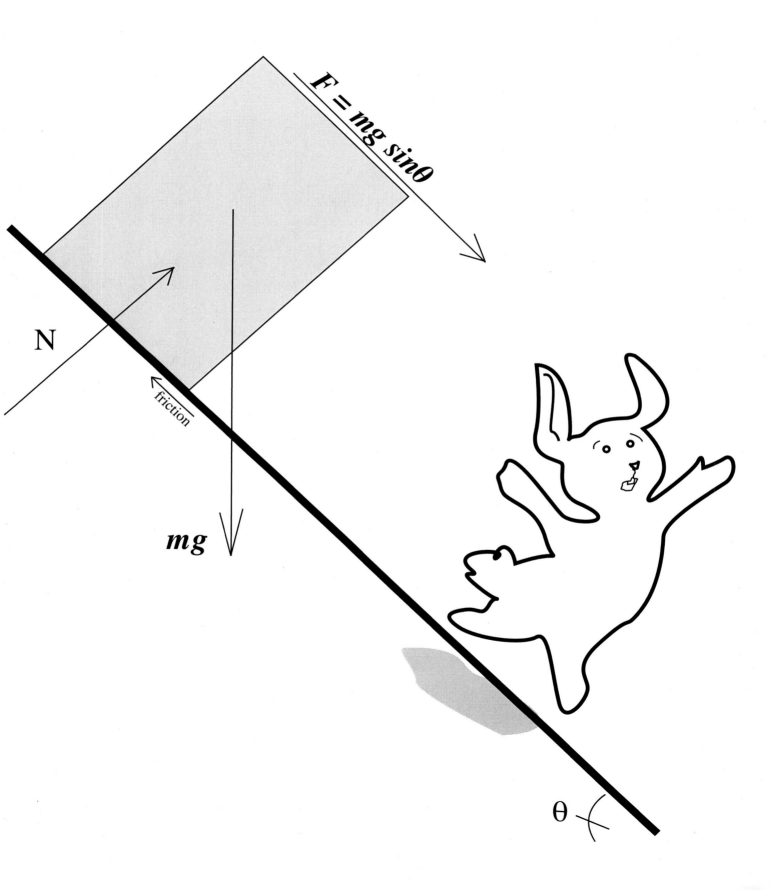

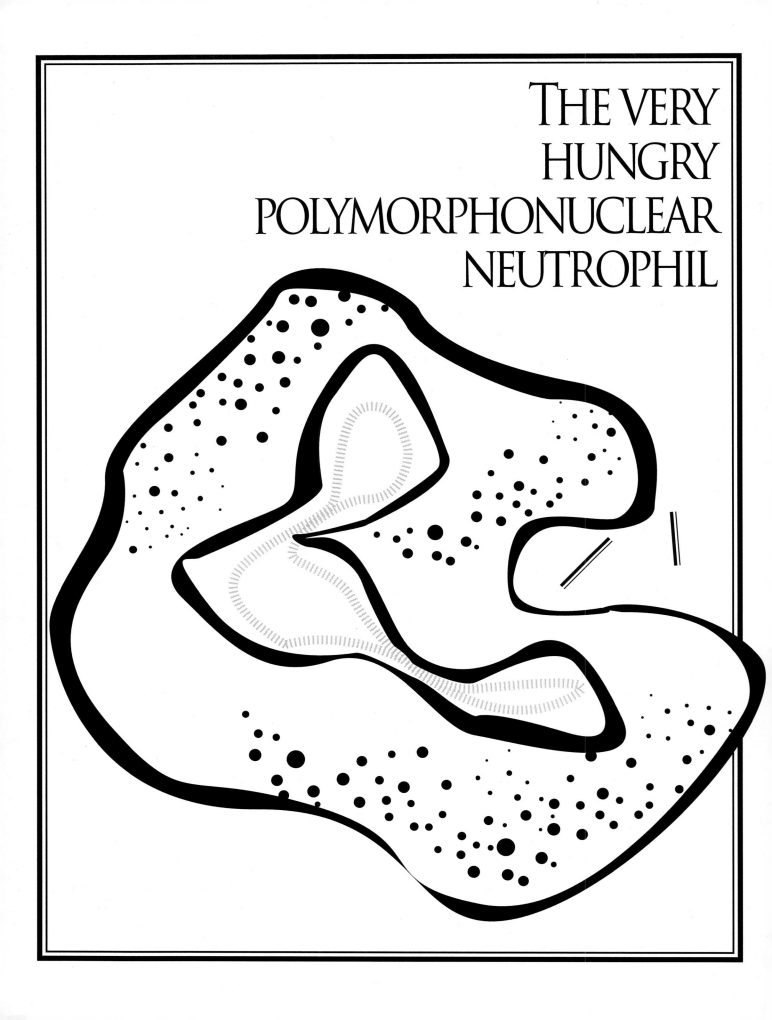

THE VERY HUNGRY POLYMORPHONUCLEAR NEUTROPHIL

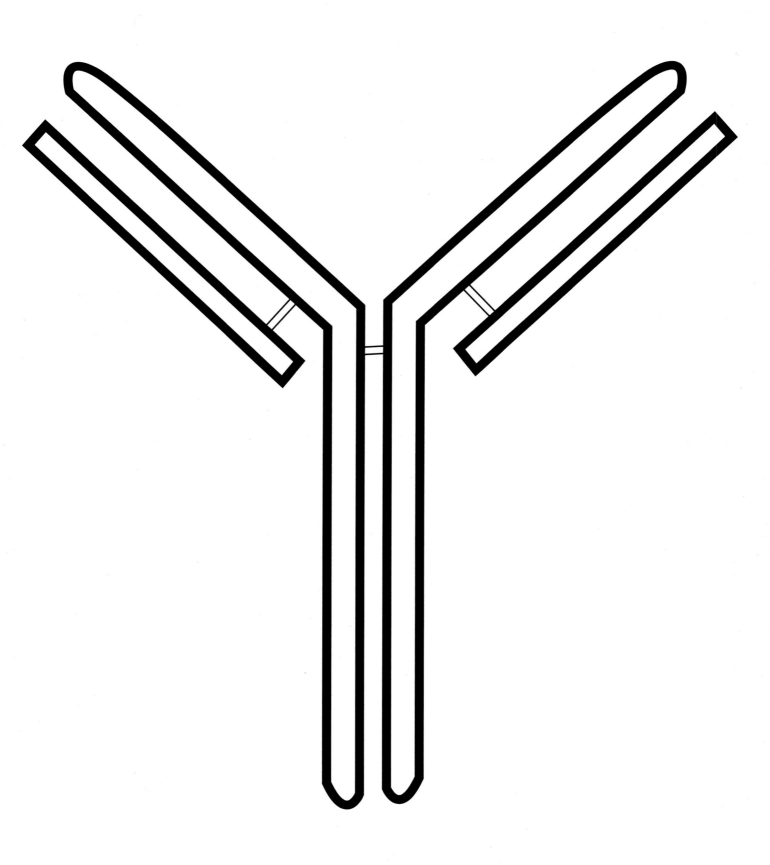

Color this stylized illustration of an antibody!
Can you draw some silly antigens for the antibody to target?

What do you see under the microscope? Draw a picture of it!

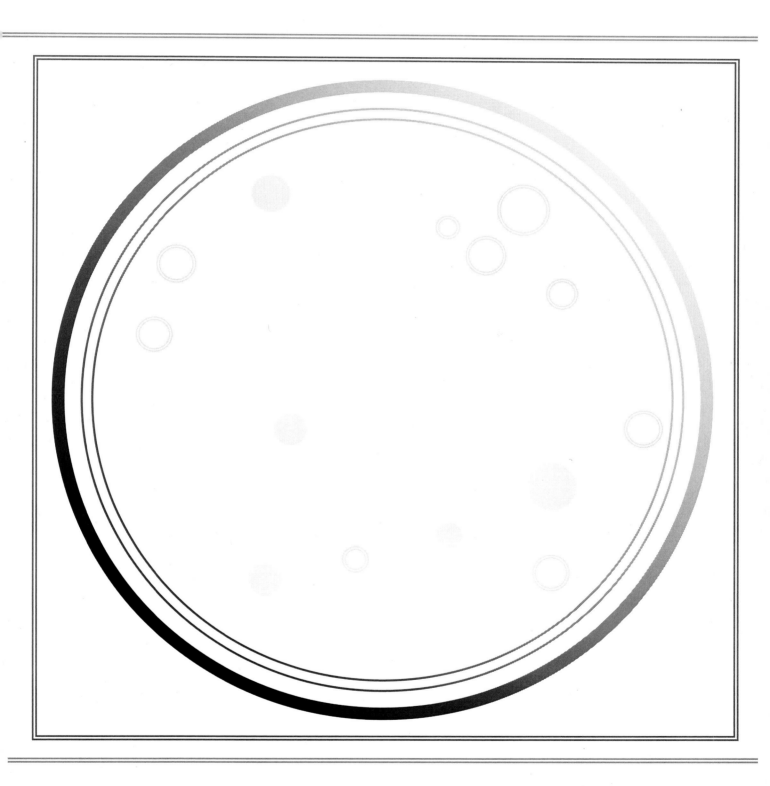

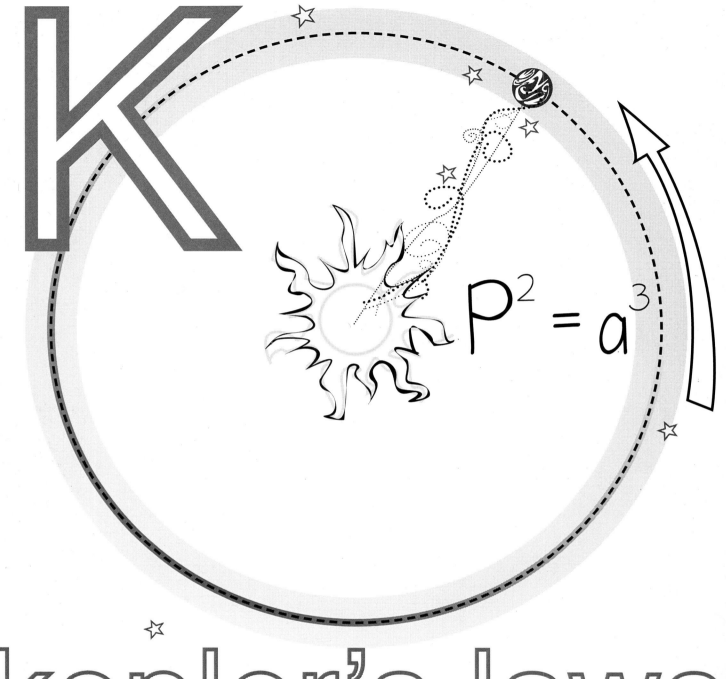

K

$$P^2 = a^3$$

kepler's laws

Kepler wanted to know all about the planets. How do they move around the sun? What does their path look like? Why is their path like that, and what does it tell us about the planet? Now almost 400 years later, astronomers use Kepler's work to learn about planets and things that are very, very far away. Thanks, Kepler!

Yes, eukaryotes are terrific with their complex organelles and fancy nuclei and their being the foundation for all complex life on earth. But just for today, let's **color and decorate the prokaryotes!**

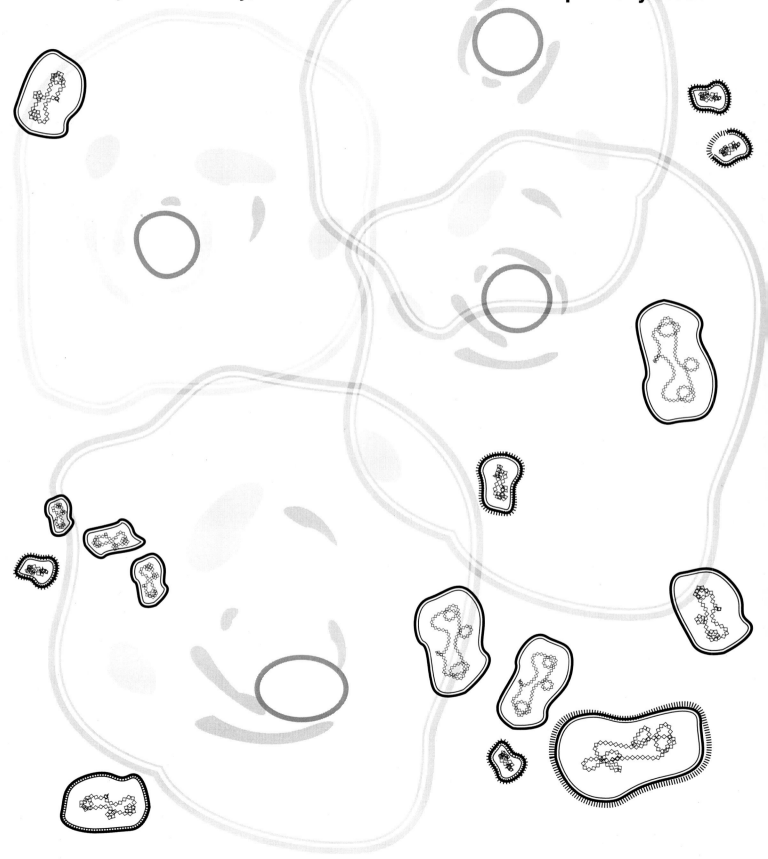

Hey, Earth! You make a better door than a window! When the earth gets in between the moon and the sun, the earth blocks the sun's light from shining directly on the moon.

lunar eclipse

M

Mandelbrot was a great mathematician. How great? He was great enough to have this very famous fractal set named after him. Maybe someday you will have a fractal set named after you! In fact, you're ahead of the game if your name is Julia. Or Sierpinski.

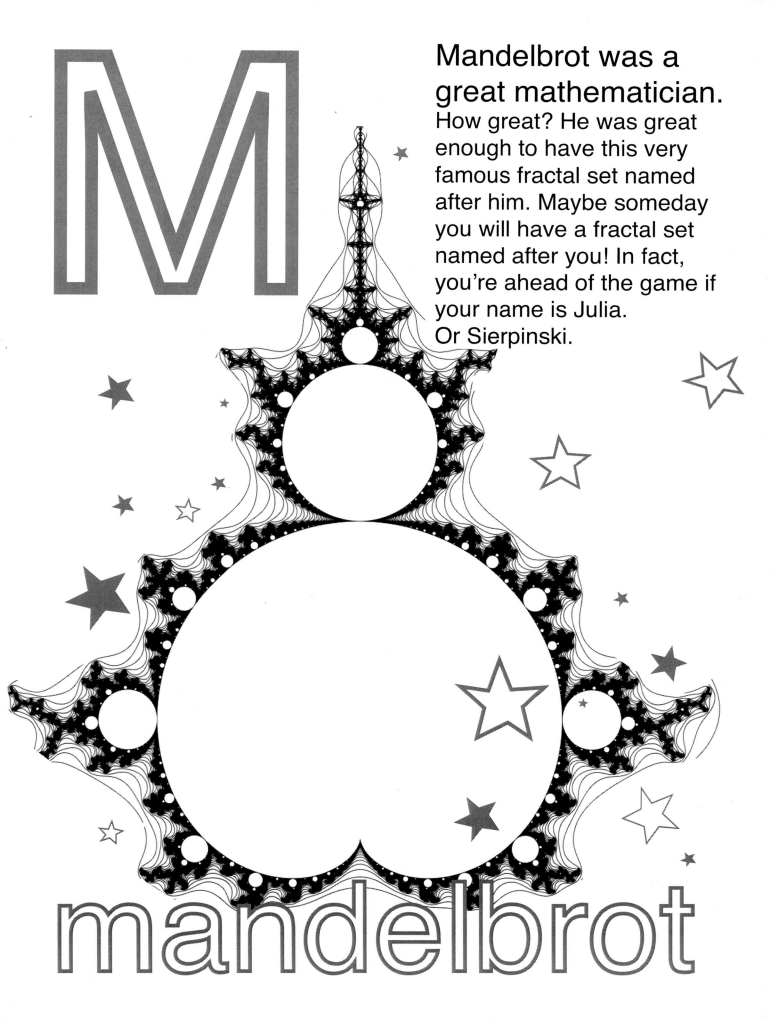

mandelbrot

Help Lucy get her PhD!

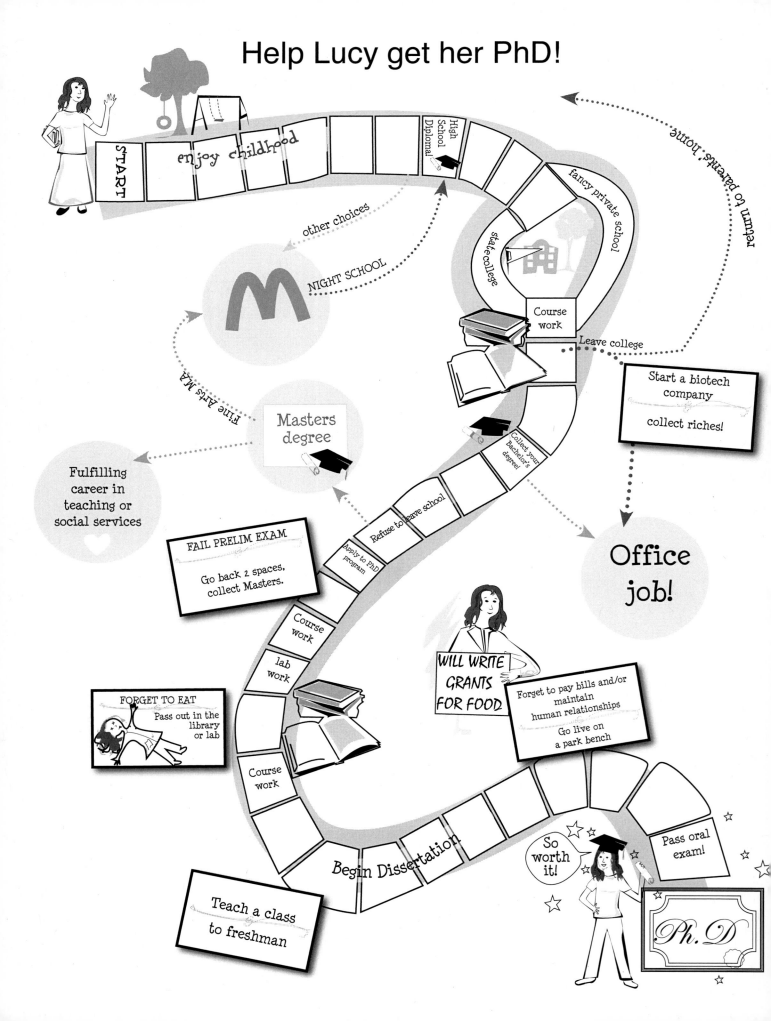

N neuron

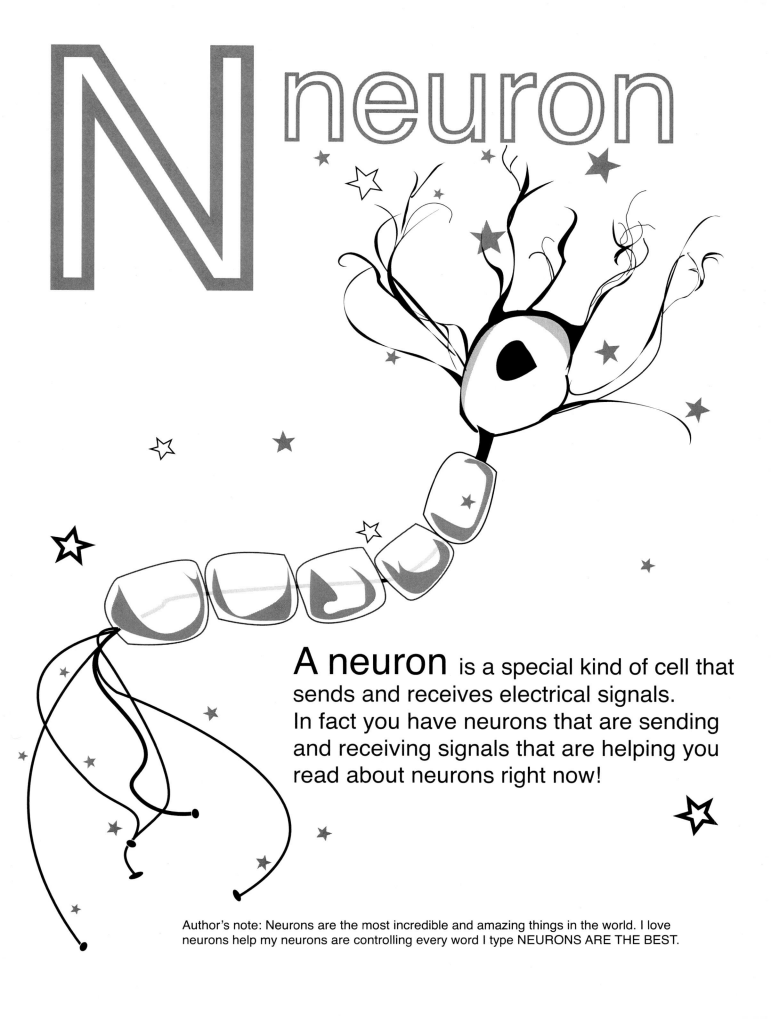

A **neuron** is a special kind of cell that sends and receives electrical signals.
In fact you have neurons that are sending and receiving signals that are helping you read about neurons right now!

Author's note: Neurons are the most incredible and amazing things in the world. I love neurons help my neurons are controlling every word I type NEURONS ARE THE BEST.

An oscillating current is a type of electrical current that changes direction. In other words, it oscillates. They weren't super creative when they came up with the name for oscillating current.

Trace the oscillation!

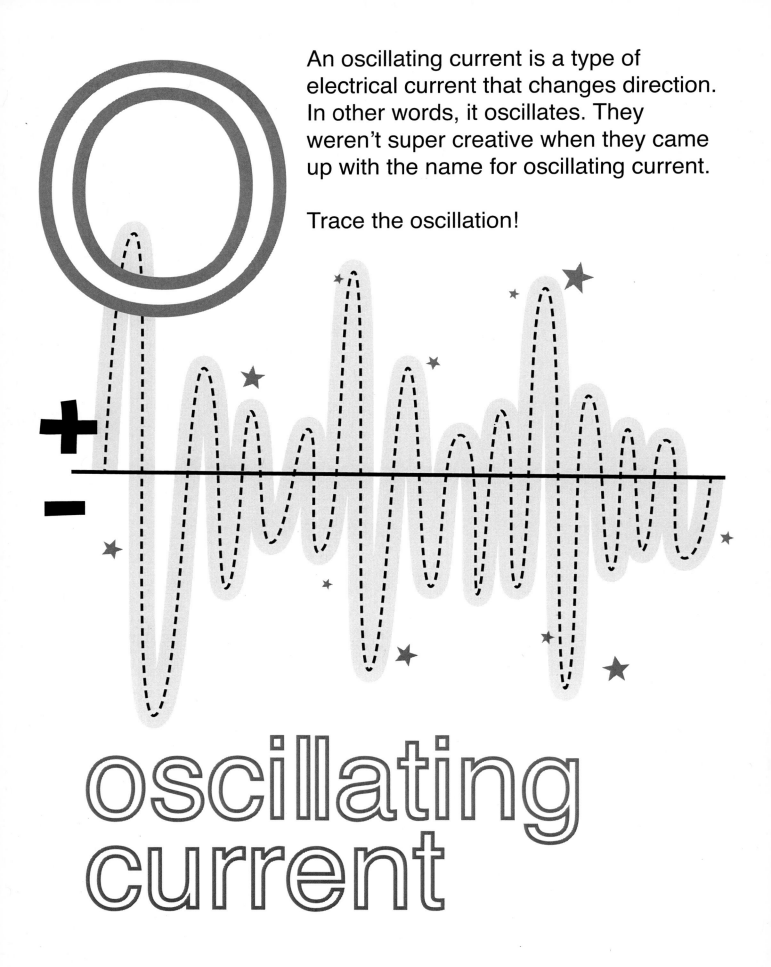

oscillating current

Help Lucy write her grant proposal!

The purpose of this experiment is:

Specific Goals:
  *

  *

Methodology and research design:

This project is important because:

Proposed time line:

"RAWR!! I'm going to eat you!"

"What? But you won't exist until the late cretaceous period. By then I'll have died and my remains will be fossilized, reabsorbed into the surrounding environment, or possibly even converted into fuel of some sort. In all cases I will be inedible.

...And what's this weird stuff on the ground?"

What will you grow in these petri dishes?

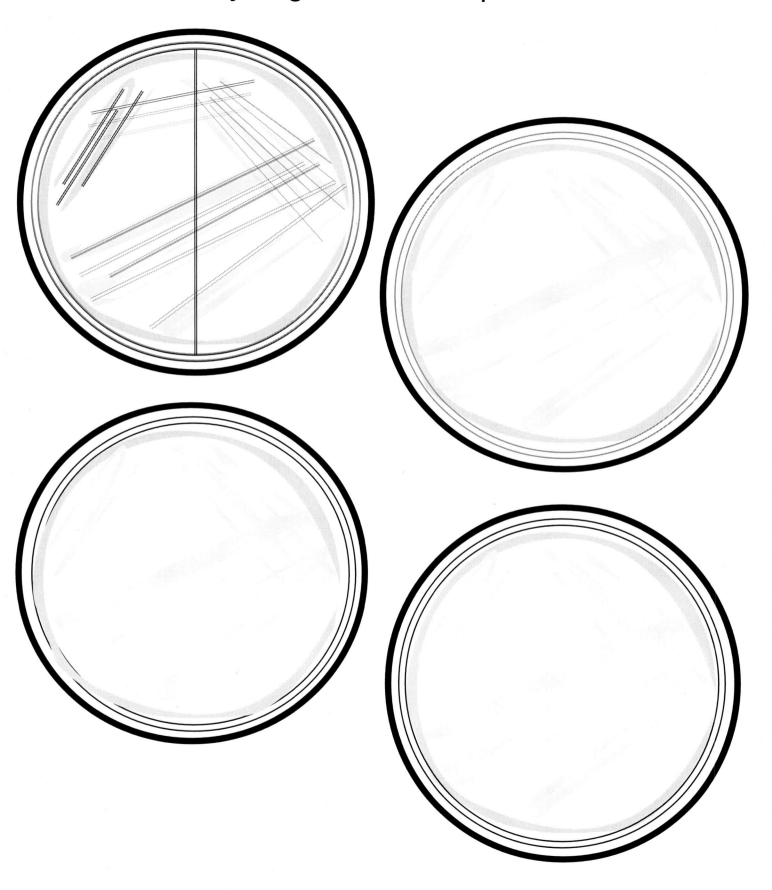

Color the pH test paper rainbow!

Universal
Indicator Paper
pH1 - pH14

1 - Red
2 - Reddish orange
3 - Orange
4 - Orangey yellow
5 - Yellow
6 - Slightly brighter yellow
7 - Greenish yellow

8 - Yellowish green
9 - Green
10 - Greenish blue
11 - Blue
12 - Dark blue
13 - Darker blue
14 - Purple

P

Sometimes people notice that two things tend to happen together. We say those things are positively correlated. Thunder and lightning, peanut butter and chocolate, age and height are all things that have a positive correlation.

positive correlation

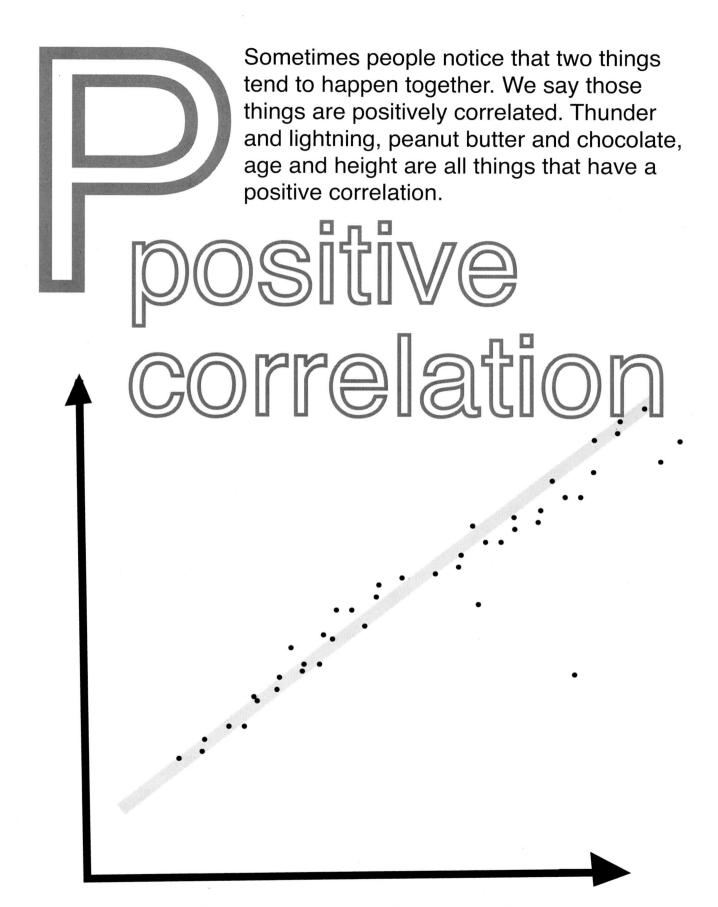

Don't forget to label your axes!

Which moth will the bird eat?
Help all the moths camouflage so they can hide!

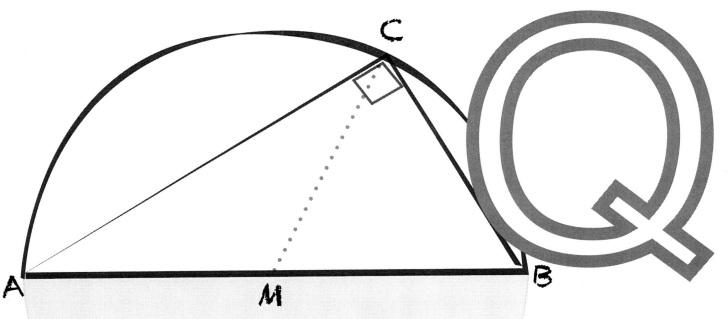

Let M be the center of the circle, diameter=AB

Then AM = BM = CM, & AMC & BMC are isosceles.

If $\angle BMC = \alpha$ then $\angle MCB = 90 - \dfrac{\alpha}{2}$

and $\angle CMA = 180 - \alpha$

Therefore $\angle ACM = \dfrac{\alpha}{2}$ and $\angle ACB = \angle MCB + \angle ACM = 90$

★QED★

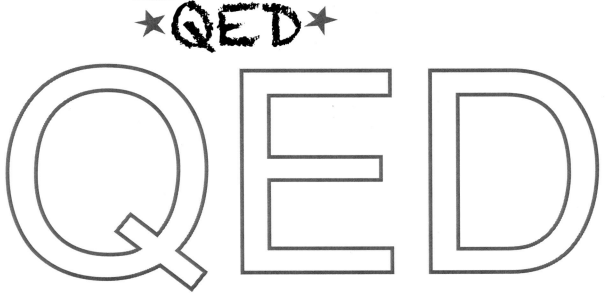

Q.E.D. is Latin for *"which is what I needed to prove."* It can also
be translated to mean "Like I said." or "BOOM!"
The next time you are trying to convince your parents of
something, tell them all of your reasons and then at the end
say "Q.E.D." and haha! they won't be able to argue with that.

Can you guess which one of these smart young ladies is going to be an engineer?

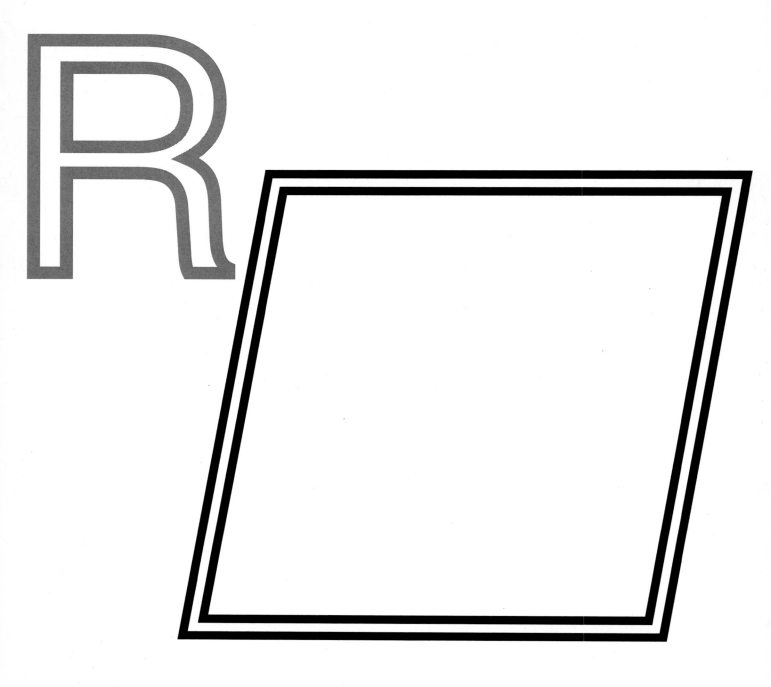

R

rhombus

The word rhombus sounds like it should mean a kind of dance. Or an endangered animal. Oh or! It could mean a type of vehicle that carries lots of passengers. But no, sorry, the word actually means a four-sided parallelogram where all four sides are equal length. You know what's a really good rhombus? A SQUARE.

The word stratum is Latin for a covering layer. Stratus clouds look like big soft blankets that cover up the sky.

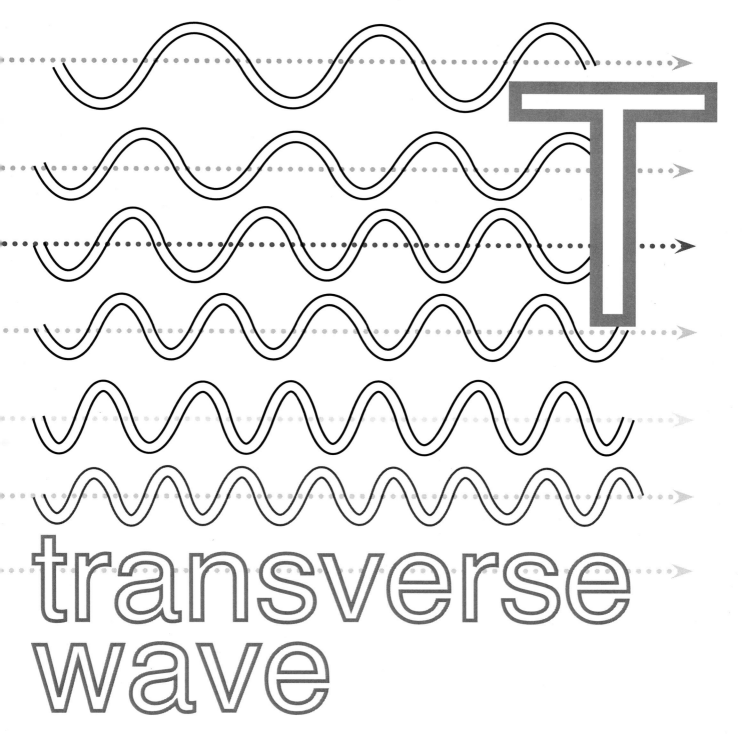

transverse wave

In olden times every kid knew about transverse waves, because back then telephones had long curly cords connecting them to the wall. There weren't any video games or safety regulations, and so a fun thing to do was to play with the cord. We'd whip the cord up and down and up and down until waves formed in the cord that looked like this: WWWWWWW Woo-Ooo-Wooo-Ooo-Wooo-oooo. That's a transverse wave!

Place your hand here:

Millions of tiny particles called Neutrinos just zipped right through your hand. Did you feel them?

No, don't worry! Neutrinos are very weakly interactive.

Draw something that is made of ATOMS!

U uvula

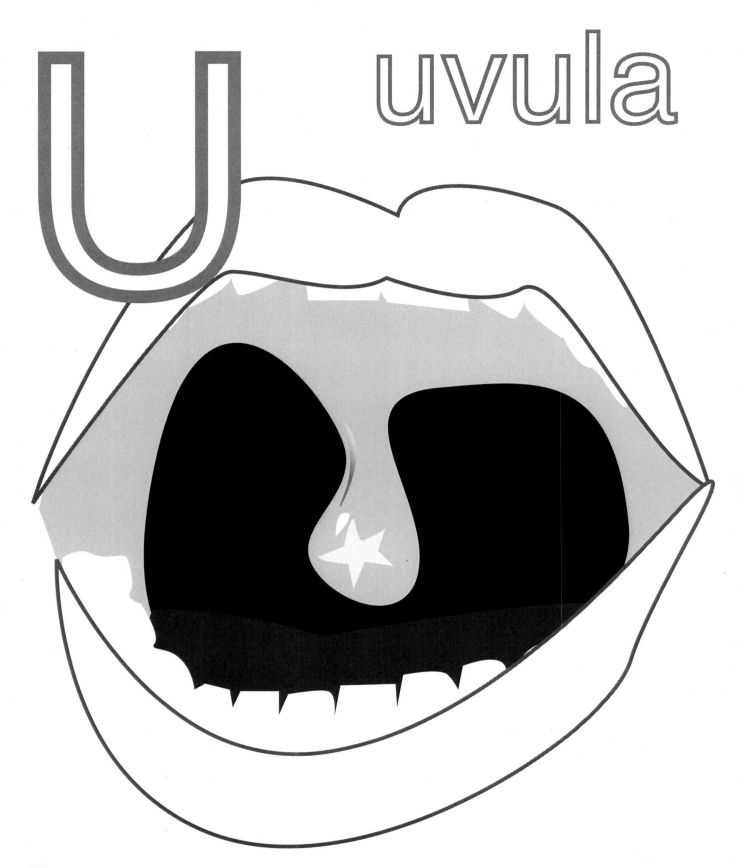

The uvula is that funny-looking bulby thing that hangs down at the back of your throat. It helps you talk and sing. Lalala!

V virus

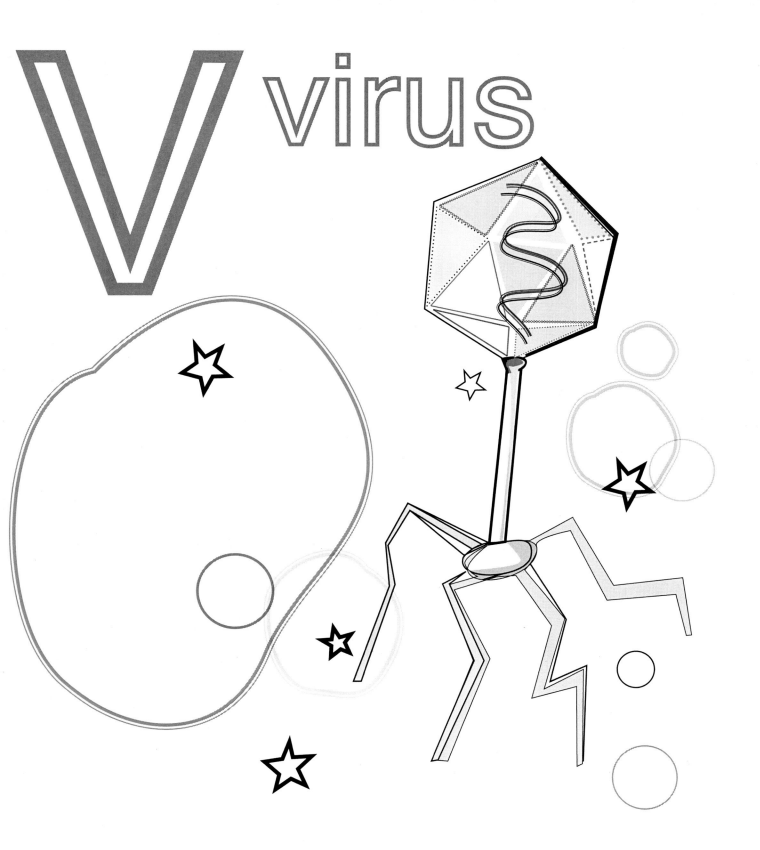

A virus is a tiny, ill-mannered thing that invades the cells of other creatures and then makes copies of itself. The invasion makes animals and people sick. Isn't that rude? Viruses don't care!

Are these atoms balanced? Fix the ones that are not balanced.
Then draw a line between each atom and its symbol. It will be fun!

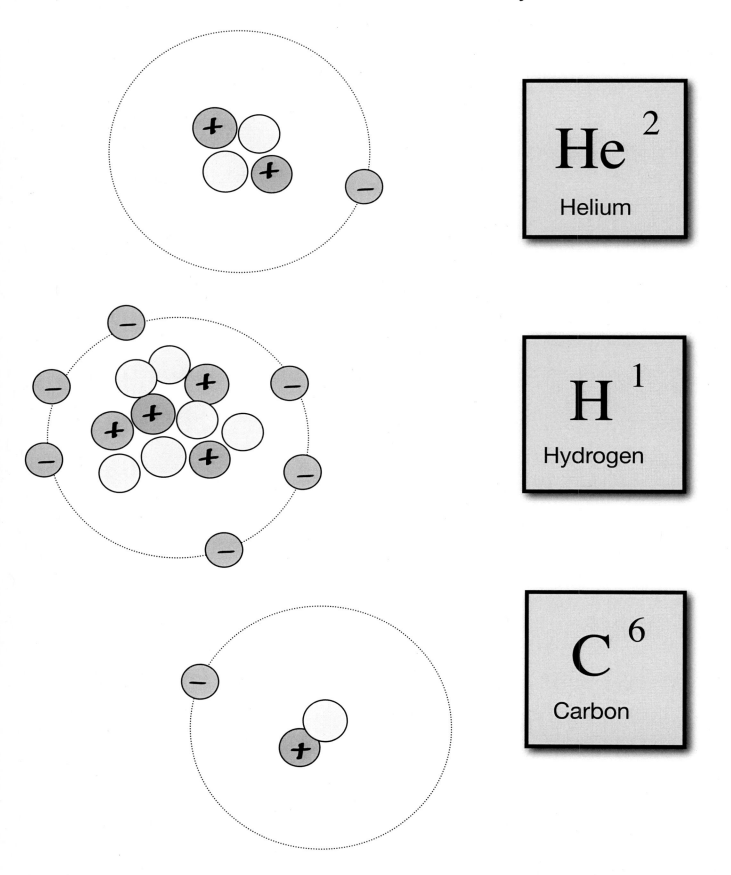

He ^{2}

Helium

H ^{1}

Hydrogen

C ^{6}

Carbon

water cycle

All of the water on Earth spends time in rivers and streams, the air, the ice caps, the oceans, and the cells of plants and animals. Every drop of water has gone through this cycle zillions of times. Next time you pour a glass of water, remember that you might be about to share a drink with dinosaurs!

xylem

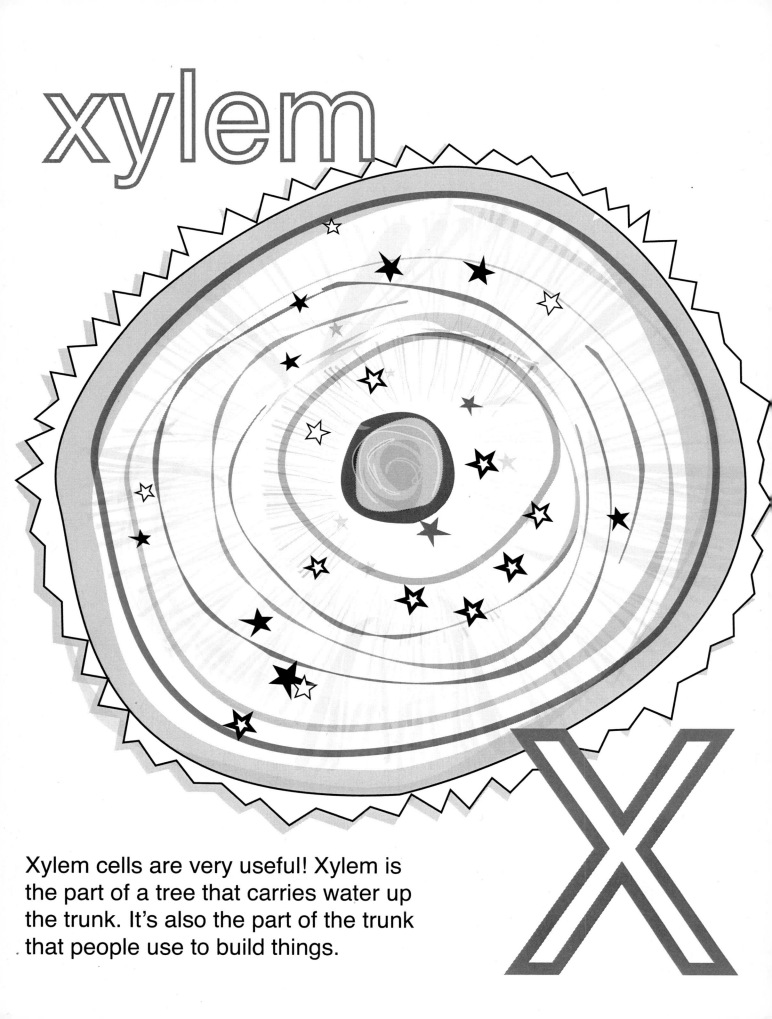

Xylem cells are very useful! Xylem is the part of a tree that carries water up the trunk. It's also the part of the trunk that people use to build things.

X

GOODNIGHT, LAB

In the great green room

there is a telephone and a red balloon.

There are three little postdocs sitting on chairs

looking into three little compound microscopes

and breathing filtered air.

There's a professor whose expectations are huge

And a digital high-speed micro centrifuge.

There's a batch of flies exhibiting mutations

and one emergency eye wash station.

Goodnight, room.

Goodnight, post docs.

Goodnight, microscopes.

Goodnight, lab manager.

Goodnight, fruit flies.

Goodnight, centrifuge.

Goodnight, eye wash station.

Goodnight, data!

Goodnight, clean air!

Goodnight noises everywhere.

Help Lucy calculate her debt!

Tuition/year $ [   ]

+ Fees, books, and supplies/year $ [   ]

+ living expenses $ [   ]

[_ _ _ _ _ _ _ _]

x 10 years

+ (5% interest per year x 10 years) $

Still totally worth it!

Ms. Lucy Smart

STATEMENT FOR MARCH 2025

total amount due: [...............]

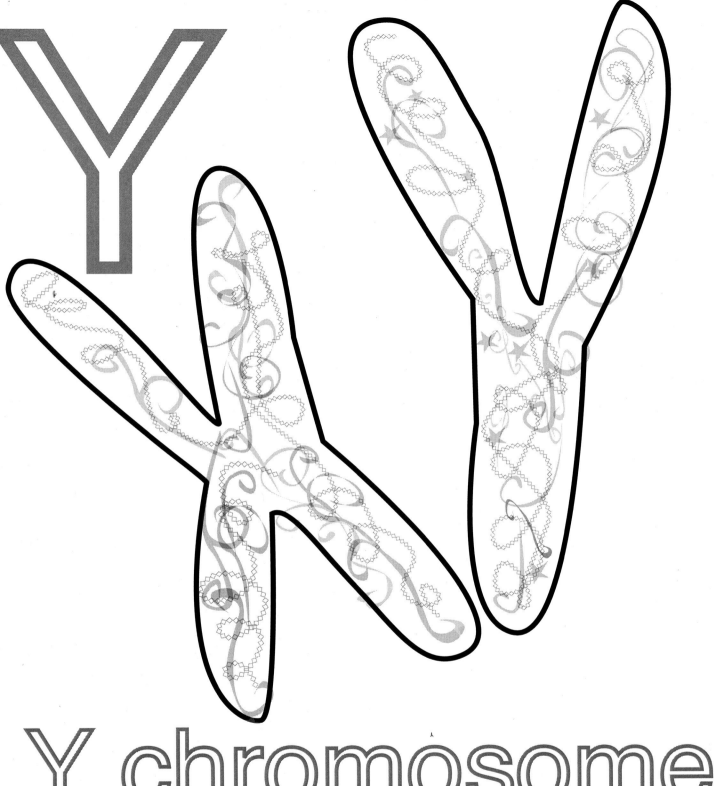

Y chromosome

A chromosome is a blob made out of DNA coils. Some are shaped like the letter X, and some are shaped like the letter Y. Most girls are born with two X chromosomes and most boys are born with one X and one Y.

Can you resist gender norms and color the Y chromosome pink?

Zzoological oddity

The platypus is a mammal that lays eggs and has a long bill like a duck. She can also inject poison into anyone who annoys her, so no one wants to tell her that she isn't following the rules about mammals.